√ **W9-AJT-781**

The HomeBuilders

C O U P L E S   S E R I E S

"Unless the Lord builds the house,
they labor in vain who build it."
Psalm 127:1

BUILDING
TEAMWORK IN
MARRIAGE

Study Guide

Lucile's
Christian Supplies
And Hobbies Center

Box 187 893-4641 AKRON, INDIANA 46910

Robert Lewis

Family : Living Under The Same Leaking Roof
Lifestyle Small Group Series
        Peter Menconi, Richard Peace
        & Lyman Coleman

How to
Let the Lord
Build Your House
and not labor in vain

The Family Ministry is a ministry of Campus Crusade for Christ International, a evangelical Christian organization founded in 1951 by Dr. Bill Bright. The Family Ministry was started in 1976 to help fulfill the Great Commission by strengthening marriages and families and then equipping them to go to the world with the Gospel of Jesus Christ. Our Family Life Conference, known as "A Weekend to Remember," is held in most major cities throughout the United State and is one of the fastest-growing marriage conferences in America today. Information on all resources offered by the Family Ministry may be obtained b either writing or calling us at the address and telephone number listed below.

■

The HomeBuilders Couples Series: A small-group Bible study series dedicated to making your family all that God intended.

BUILDING TEAMWORK IN MARRIAGE—STUDY GUIDE
ISBN 0-8499-8342-8

Scripture quotations used are from the New American Standard Bible, copyright 1960, 1962, 1963, 1968, 1971 by The Lockman Foundation, used by permission.

Dennis Rainey, National Director
Family Ministry
P.O. Box 23840
Little Rock, AR 72221-3840
(501) 223-8663

A Ministry of Campus Crusade for Christ International
Dr. Bill Bright, President and Founder

CONTENTS

ACKNOWLEDGMENTS

A hearty "thank you" and a special word of recognition needs to be recorded here to those supportive individuals who helped make this Bible study a reality.

My wife, Sherard, of course, tops any list. No one has given my life more encouragement and energy than she has. No one provides more support to endeavors like this one than she does. Sherard is chiefly responsible for so much of the "right" in my life. A helper indeed!

Dennis Rainey is the visionary behind **The HomeBuilders Couples Series**. Thank you, Dennis, for your vote of confidence in allowing me this opportunity. You are a great friend, and I count it a real privilege to be serving next to you.

As my personal assistant, Ann Blair has been indispensable. It's not just that she typed and retyped many revisions of the original manuscript . . . it's the attitude with which she did so. Ann also offered many helpful suggestions.

I owe Julie Denker of the Family Ministry many thank yous, too. Julie helped push this project to completion. She also spent great amounts of time shaping this study into its final form with her excellent revisionist hands.

I also want to single out Ray Williams. Ray is a special friend who has consistently been available as a sounding board for new ideas and honest evaluation. Ray, I appreciate your insight and your patience.

To the many groups around the country who first piloted this project . . . thanks for your feedback. You *did* make significant contributions. I especially want to thank Ed and Judy Ligon for their encouragement here.

Finally, I want to thank a gracious group of people known as Fellowship Bible Church in Little Rock, Arkansas. It has been a unique and special privilege to serve you these past ten years. To you I dedicate this study.

How to
Let the Lord
Build Your House
and not labor in vain

FOREWORD

Webster defines the word *crisis* as a turning point, a critical turn in a disease. As we move into the 1990s, we are experiencing a crisis in the roles of husbands and wives.

The turning point has occurred because of a massive movement to redefine what it means to be a man or a woman, a husband or a wife. If we who are in the Christian community are to survive the onslaught of this movement, then we must return to our biblical moorings for stability and strength. That is why this study in **The HomeBuilders Couples Series** is so important—it gives couples a biblical definition and description of the husband's and wife's responsibility.

Robert Lewis is on target in one of the hottest issues facing Christian marriages. He is a profound biblical thinker, and his insights on the "battle of the sexes" will help you understand your mate in new ways. Because of his vast experience with couples over nearly twenty years, his practical solutions are workable and achievable. Robert's material will truly liberate many marriages to become all that God intended.

DENNIS RAINEY

The HomeBuilders

C O U P L E S   S E R I E S

"Unless the Lord builds the house,
they labor in vain who build it."
Psalm 127:1

What Is The HomeBuilders Couples Series?

Do you remember the first time you fell in love? That junior high—or elementary school—"crush" stirred your affections with little or no effort on your part. We use the term "falling in love" to describe the phenomenon of suddenly discovering our emotions have been captured by someone delightful.

Unfortunately, our society tends to make us think that all loving relationships should be equally as effortless. Thus, millions of couples, Christians included, approach their marriage certain that the emotions they feel will carry them through any difficulties. And millions of couples quickly learn that a good marriage does not automatically happen.

Otherwise intelligent people, who would not think of buying a car, investing money, or even going to the grocery store without some initial planning, enter into marriage with no plan of how to make their marriage succeed.

But God has already provided the plan, a set of blueprints for a truly godly marriage. His plan is designed to enable two people to grow together in a mutually satisfying relationship, and then to look beyond their own marriage to others. Ignoring this plan leads only to isolation and separation between husband and wife, the pattern so evident in the majority of homes today. Even when great energy is expended, failure to follow God's blueprints results in wasted effort, bitter disappointment—and, in far too many cases, divorce.

In response to this need in marriages today, the Family Ministry of Campus Crusade for Christ is developing a series of small group Bible studies called **The HomeBuilders Couples Series**. This series is designed to answer one question for couples:

How Do You Build a Distinctively Christian Marriage?

It is our hope that in answering this question with the biblical blueprints for building a home, we will see the development of growing, thriving marriages filled with the love of Jesus Christ.

The Family Ministry of Campus Crusade for Christ is committed to strengthening your family. We hope **The HomeBuilders Couples Series** will assist you and your church as it equips couples in building godly homes.

This study, **Building Teamwork In Marriage**, is designed to provide the basis upon which a godly marriage can be built. It is composed of seven sessions, each built around a concept that will enrich your marriage in the weeks that follow.

The Bible: Your Blueprints for a Godly Marriage

> The Bible is alive, it speaks to me;
> it has feet, it runs after me;
> it has hands, it lays its hold on me.
>
> Martin Luther

You will notice as you proceed through this study that the Bible is referred to frequently as the final authority on the issues of life and marriage. Although written centuries ago, this Book still speaks clearly and powerfully about the conflicts and struggles faced by men and women. The Bible is God's Word, His blueprints for building a godly home and for dealing with the practical issues of living.

While Scripture has only one primary interpretation, there may be several appropriate applications. Some of the passages used in this series were not originally written with marriage in mind, but they can be applied practically to the husband-wife relationship.

We encourage you to have a Bible with you for each session. The New American Standard is an excellent English translation which is strongly recommended for this session.

Ground Rules for These Sessions

These sessions are designed to be enjoyable and informative—and nonthreatening. Three simple ground rules will help insure that everyone feels comfortable and gets the most out of the series:

1. Share nothing about your marriage that will embarrass your mate.

2. You may pass on any question you do not want to answer.

3. Each time between sessions, complete the **HomeBuilders Project** (a few questions for each couple to discuss). Share one result at the next group meeting.

Resources

I recommend these outstanding aids to maximize your **HomeBuilders** study experience:

1. If you are doing this as a couple, I would recommend one Study Guide for each spouse. The Leader's Guide would also be very beneficial.

2. If you have been to the Family Life Conference, you will find the **Family Life Conference Manual** to be a useful tool as you go through **The HomeBuilders Couples Series**.

HOMEBUILDERS PRINCIPLES

HomeBuilders Principle #1: The Scripture will make you wise in the way you live with your mate (Psalm 119:97–100).

HomeBuilders Principle #2: True equality in a marriage is achieved when a husband and a wife come to understand, appreciate, and honor each other's differentness.

HomeBuilders Principle #3: The greatest need a woman has in her marriage is to be loved RIGHTLY.

HomeBuilders Principle #4: Other than a man's relationship with the Lord, few things tell a man more about himself than does the respect of his wife.

HomeBuilders Principle #5: It is crucial that a husband's leadership role be accurately defined before it can be accurately fulfilled.

HomeBuilders Principle #6: Submission is a woman's spiritual *response* that encourages her husband to fulfill his spiritual role. Submission is essential to the man's success as a servant-leader.

HomeBuilders Principle #7: It is crucial that a wife's role as helper and homemaker be accurately defined before it can be accurately fulfilled.

HomeBuilders Principle #8: Honor and praise are the masculine counterparts to submission. They are essential to the wife's success as a helper-homemaker.

HomeBuilders Principle #9: The Holy Spirit will be faithful to remind us of God's Word if we are faithful in learning it.

HomeBuilders Principle #10: The fuel that most often energizes the flesh is our world (1 John 2:15/Jude 19).

HomeBuilders Principle #11: The Holy Spirit helps fulfill in us what God requires of us in marriage.

HomeBuilders Principle #12: The fuel that most often energizes the Spirit is God's Word (2 Timothy 3:16/Colossians 3:16a).

omeBuilders Principle #13: A husband and wife can resolve their ender differences, respond to unique needs, and fulfill respective les only as they submit by faith to God's Spirit and live under His ecial influence (Ephesians 5:18).

omeBuilders Principle #14: You will leave in your children what u have lived out in your home.

omeBuilders Principle #15: A wise couple knows what life's most omising investments are.

The HomeBuilders

C O U P L E S   S E R I E S

"Unless the Lord builds the house,
they labor in vain who build it."
Psalm 127:1

*Men and women are more than
noticeably different. Understanding
and responding to these deeper
differences is vital to building a
good marriage.*

1. Introduce yourself to the group by sharing the following information:

a. name
b. occupation
c. years married

d. number of children (if any)
e. one expectation you have in joining this study

Use the space below to record your new knowledge of the others in the group.

_____

_____

_____

_____

_____

_____

_____

An alternative to the previous **WARM UP** is the following exercise. You may choose to use this if your group is well acquainted with one another.

2. Complete the following statement: "My marriage has taught me ome important things about the opposite sex. For instance . . ."

_____

_____

_____

_____

/hen you share what you have written, be sure to add *how* you ame to this conclusion.

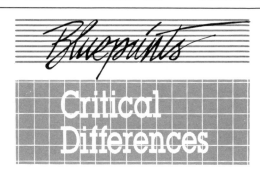

I. Creative Differences

> And God created man in His own image, in the image of God He
> created Him, male and female He created them (Genesis 1:27).

It was a wonderful thing God did when He divided man into "male
and female." He called His two creations "very good" (Genesis 1:31).
The differences separating man as male and woman as female were
intended to usher in many special blessings (Genesis 1:28).
Unfortunately, with the fall of man, the blessings of the sexes became
more a battle between the sexes. The unique qualities with which
God endowed each gender now gave rise to misunderstanding and
contention rather than completion and power.

To recapture what has been lost, we must first develop an
understanding of and then an appreciation for God's design of mankind
as "male and female." We are each married to someone who is both
like us and yet unlike us. We each bear God's image but we express
that image differently . . . as male and female. So to accurately
comprehend and ultimately love the special differences these terms
imply is of vital importance to any marriage. As we all know, these
differences are not theoretical in nature but intensely practical.
Therefore, becoming a student of the opposite sex is a great starting
place for building a good marriage (or rebuilding a damaged one.)

I. Practical Differences

elow are a series of general observations social scientists have
ade regarding male and female differences.[1] Discuss with your
roup how each of these differences has at times manifested itself in
our marriage. What misunderstandings (if any) have resulted
ecause of them?

A. Women have a greater need of belonging; men have a greater
eed of achieving.

B. Women are more sensitive than men; the expressing of feelings
 more important to them.

C. Men tend to see their work as extensions of themselves; women
re apt to see their husband and family that way.

D. Men are more goal-oriented; women more need-oriented.

E. Men are more focused in their thinking; women are more
tuitive in their thinking.

F. Women tend to require more frequent reassurance.

G. Men are more physical; women are more relational.

There will always be exceptions to any general observation. Exceptions, however,
ould not negate the truthfulness of these general observations nor undermine their
lpfulness. For an excellent discussion on men's and women's differences, see Steven B.
ark's book, *Man and Woman In Christ: An Examination of the Roles of Men and
omen in Light of Scripture and the Social Sciences* (Ann Arbor: Servant Books, 1980),
. 371–448.

III. A Call to Understanding

A. God never intended for male and female differences to divide husbands and wives or bring conflict between them. Quite the contrary; God's original intent was for us to appreciate and honor those unique qualities which our mates possess. The Scripture appeals to us to adopt this kind of perspective.

"You husbands likewise live with your wives in an understanding way, as the weaker vessel,[2] since she is a woman; and grant her honor as a fellow heir of the grace of life, so that your prayers may not be hindered" (1 Peter 3:7).

What are the two major exhortations to husbands in this passage?

1. _____

_____

2. _____

_____

B. The First Exhortation

1. How does the first exhortation in this passage call for a recognition of the differences between the sexes?

_____

_____

2. "Weaker vessel" is most probably referring to a woman's physical strength as compared to that of a man's. Men generally have more muscle than women. Selfish men have used this superior physical strength as a means of subjugating and intimidating women.

2. If this first exhortation were being addressed to wives instead of husbands, would it be stated any differently? If so, how?

_____

_____

3. The key word to living successfully with the opposite sex (whether it be a man or woman) is the word "understanding." Practically, how does one go about obtaining this understanding? What's the process?

_____

_____

4. In order to grasp this first exhortation more fully, let's focus more closely for a moment on the phrase "in an understanding way."

a. From the original Greek, the phrase is literally translated "according to knowledge." The King James Bible renders it just this way.

b. Further, the word *knowledge* in this literal rendering is often used in reference to the Scriptures.[3]

Putting these two additional thoughts together, what new insights do you gain from 1 Peter 3:7?

_____

_____

_____

_____

_____

W. F. Arndt, and F. W. Gingrich, *A Greek-English Lexicon of the New Testament* (Chicago: University of Chicago Press, 1952), p. 163.

21

5. On a scale of 1 to 10, how well do you know what the Bible says about marriage, men, and women? Please circle one.

1	2	3	4	5	6	7	8	9	10

Very Little   Great
Understanding   Understanding

(This **HomeBuilders Couples Series** study promises to add points to your score!)

6. Contrast the "understanding way" being called for by Peter in 1 Peter 3:7 (i.e., the Scripture) with the "way" of Proverbs 16:25 (the way that so many choose in living with their mates). What is this other "way"? Explain.

_____

_____

_____

> **HomeBuilders Principle #1: The Scripture will make you wise in the way you live with your mate (Psalm 119:97–100).**

C. The Second Exhortation

1. Now notice the second exhortation within 1 Peter 3:7. What major social movement has resulted in part because men have trusted in their natural instincts rather than "the way" encouraged by this scripture?

_____

_____

2. Despite their differentness, what "status" does Peter say a husband must always be reaffirming in his wife?

_____

_____

3. What are some *practical* ways a husband can do this?

_____

_____

HomeBuilders Principle #2: True equality in a marriage is achieved when a husband and a wife come to understand, appreciate, and honor each other's differentness.

V. Summary

God created unique and special differences into mankind when He created them as male and female. Understanding and responding to these special differences lays a solid foundation upon which to build a strong marriage. This session and the projects which will now follow are presented to help you start this process.

(to be completed as a couple)

Answer the following questions:

1. What areas of our marriage came to mind as a result of tonight's discussion? Why?

_____

_____

2. Wife, what is one thing your husband can do to make you feel more like an equal or "co-heir"? Tell him why this request would be important to you. He needs your feminine perspective to aid his understanding.

_____

_____

_____

3. Conclude your time by reading together the personal pledge statement on the following page:

"I pledge to you that I will use the next six weeks of this HomeBuilders study to build, strengthen, and encourage our marriage. I will make this study a priority in my schedule by faithfully keeping our "dates," working through the projects, and participating in the group discussions. You have my word on it."

(signed) _____

Will you honor your mate by making this pledge *your* special commitment to him or her for the coming weeks? If so, sign your name in the space underneath this pledge in **your mate's** study guide to document your commitment.

Each of the seven sessions in this study will end with a **MAKE A DATE**. This is the time you set aside outside each session to do the **HomeBuilders Projects** which you will find at the end of each session. This will be your *only* homework. Do not begin working on the next session until you meet together again as a group. Do only the assigned **HomeBuilders Project** between sessions.

Now conclude Session One by setting aside one hour in your schedule right now to complete **HomeBuilders Project #1**. As a couple, this project will aid you in continuing the process of building your marriage. Your leader will ask you at the next session to share one thing from this experience.

Date	Time	Location

■

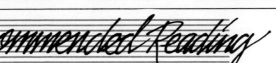

■ The Art of Understanding Your Mate   by Cecil Osborne

This book is filled with practical common sense and psychological insights. The author uses many case histories, often humorous, to help husbands and wives better understand each other and build a superior, lasting relationship.

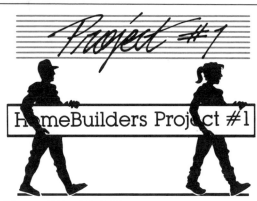

Individually—15–20 Minutes

Write out your answers to the following questions:

1. List two things you want your mate to understand about you that you feel he (or she) is unaware of because of your gender difference.

_____

_____

_____

2. List two things you are having difficulty with in understanding your mate.

_____

_____

_____

3. In what areas have these things affected the quality of your marriage?

_____

_____

_____

4. How can you communicate these things in a way that doesn't attack your mate but instead gives insight and understanding into why these things are important?

_____

_____

Interact As a Couple—30–45 Minutes

1. Read together Ephesians 4:29–32 before beginning your interaction to set the tone of your discussion.

2. Share with your mate your answers to the previous questions.

3. Listen carefully and seek to understand your mate's differentness.

4. Commit to a plan of action that will honor your mate in regard to the things that have been communicated to you. Write out your action plan below. Remember, understanding and responding to male and female differences is important to building a good marriage.

_____

_____

_____

_____

_____

Remember to bring your calendar for **MAKE A DATE** to the next session.

29

The HomeBuilders

C O U P L E S   S E R I E S

"Unless the Lord builds the house,
they labor in vain who build it."
Psalm 127:1

Women are, by creation, different from men. These differences generate needs... needs which a husband is uniquely called upon to fulfill.

1. In Session One, the discussion centered on grappling with those differences which are brought into a marriage by virtue of one partner being male and the other female. What new understanding or fresh insight did you receive in each of the following areas:

Concerning myself I discovered (or was made more aware of) . . .

_____

_____

Concerning my mate I discovered (or was made more aware of) . .

_____

_____

2. Would you share from **HomeBuilders Project #1** the action point (or part of it) you wish to take to honor your mate in the weeks to come

What Is It That Women Need Most?

A. Everyone has needs. Some of these needs, however, are of greater importance to women than they are to men. WIVES: Share what you believe these special feminine needs are. Then discuss which of these needs are the three greatest. HUSBANDS: Listen carefully! EVERYONE: Take notes!

_____

_____

_____

Our top three choices are:

_____

_____

_____

B. Colossians 3:19 says, "Husbands, love your wives, and do not be embittered against them." This verse has something special to say about a woman's needs. By way of a command it urges husbands to be active in meeting what the Bible considers the most important need a wife possesses. What is that need? How does it compare with the wives' "choices" of greatest needs?

_____

_____

II. Where Husbands Sometimes Go Wrong

Notice the contrasting phrase of Colossians 3:19. The word translated "embittered" means "to be exasperated" with.[1] It suggests a growing and deepening frustration, irritation, and anger with one's wife.

HUSBANDS: We sometimes become "embittered" with our wives because we don't understand them. Think carefully here. In what areas have you at times detected a *growing* resentment or exasperation with your wife which short-circuits the expression of your love she so needs? List one or two examples below.

_____

_____

_____

Remember that your wife as a female goes about things differently than you do as a male. Remember, too, Peter's admonition: "Husband live with your wives in an understanding way" (1 Peter 3:7).

III. How to Love Your Wife Rightly

Let's explore this basic need for "love" more closely. Certainly the word *love* means different things to different people. But in marriage, the Bible says that the love a woman needs is something *very specific*. Review this more specific description of love in Ephesians 5:25–29. We will focus on three particular qualities that define the kind of love a wife needs.

1. H. G. Liddell, and Scott, *Greek-English Lexicon* (Oxford: Clarendon Press, 1975), p. 639.

A. The First Quality

1. The first specific quality defining a husband's love for his wife is found in verse 25 with the comparison of Christ's love for the church. What characteristic of love stands out in this comparison?

_____

_____

2. In order for Christ to love the church the way He did, whom did He often have to say "no" to? (For help, see also Philippians 2:3–5 and Matthew 20:28.)

_____

_____

3. When a man responds to a woman in this way, what does this kind of love say to her?

_____

_____

B. The Second Quality

1. A second specific quality defining a husband's love for his wife is found within verses 27–28a. How do these verses suggest that a husband's love should specifically promote, develop, and enhance his wife's life?

_____

_____

What key words stand out in verse 27 in this regard? For instance, how would you practically define the phrase "in all *her* glory" (v. 27) as far as a wife is concerned?

_____

_____

2. How could these verses be used to address the low self-esteem problem and inferior feelings that so often plague a woman's life?[2] (A review of letters C and F under "Practical Differences" in Session One might be helpful in answering this question.)

_____

_____

_____

_____

_____

3. What is the blueprint a husband should follow in seeking his wife's best (see v. 26)?

_____

_____

_____

C. The Third Quality

1. A final specific quality that should mark a husband's love for his wife is found in verses 28b–29. Two important and positive "action"

---

2. As reported in James Dobson's book, _What Wives Wish Their Husbands Knew About Women_ (Wheaton: Tyndale House Publishers, 1986), pp. 22–41. Note the following excerpt: "If I could write a prescription for the women of the world, I would provide each one of them with a healthy dose of self-esteem and personal worth (taken three times a day unt. the symptoms disappear). I have no doubt that this is their greatest need. . . . If they felt equal with men in personal worth, they would not need to be equivalent to men in responsibility. If they could only bask in the dignity and status granted them by the Creator, then their femininity would be valued as their greatest asset, rather than scorne as an old garment to be discarded. Without question, the future of a nation depends on how it sees its women, and I hope we will teach our little girls to be glad they were chose by God for the special pleasures of womanhood" (p. 35).

words mark out this final aspect of love in verse 29. Fill in the blanks below with these two critical verbs:

_____ meaning **"to provide for"**

and

_____ meaning **"to protect and take care of"**

A helpful insight into this second word comes from its usage to describe "birds covering their young with their feathers."[3] "The need for security is one of the strongest emotional needs a woman possesses."[4]

2. HUSBANDS: Discuss several practical ways you as a husband can love your wife by nourishing and cherishing her?

_____

_____

_____

_____

. WIVES: What helpful suggestions would you offer?

_____

_____

V. Summary

Through her husband a woman's special need of love is to be fulfilled. His love for her should be the kind that specifically (1) declares her importance and worth, (2) seeks her personal development, and (3) provides for her a strong sense of security. Nothing less will do.

W. E. Vine, *Expository Dictionary of New Testament Words* (Old Tappan, NJ: Fleming Revell Co., 1966), p. 184.
Cecil Osborne, *The Art of Understanding Your Mate* (Grand Rapids: Zondervan Publishing House, 1977), p. 50.

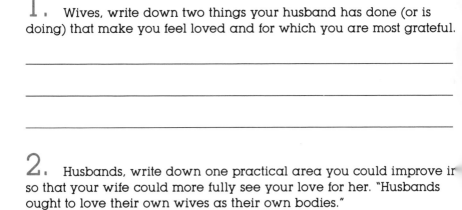

(to be completed as a couple)

1. Wives, write down two things your husband has done (or is doing) that make you feel loved and for which you are most grateful.

_____

_____

_____

2. Husbands, write down one practical area you could improve in so that your wife could more fully see your love for her. "Husbands ought to love their own wives as their own bodies."

_____

_____

3. Share your conclusions with one another.

> **HomeBuilders Principle #3: The greatest need a woman has in her marriage is to be loved RIGHTLY.**

Make a Date

Make a date with your mate to meet in the next few days to complete **HomeBuilders Project #2**.

_____ _____ _____
Date   Time   Location

Recommended Reading

(for husbands only)

**What Wives Wish Their Husbands
Knew about Women**   by Dr. James Dobson

In this classic bestseller, Dr. Dobson identifies the ten main causes of dissatisfaction and unhappiness among women in the marriage relationship.

■

39

Individually—15–20 Minutes

1. HUSBAND: Carefully review Session Two.

2. WIFE: Complete the following project, circling the numbers that apply and filling in the blanks:

Because of my husband's love . . .

a. I feel extremely valuable.

1	2	3	4	5	6	7	8	9	10
Rarely				Some of the time					Always

Please explain: _____

_____

_____

If there are problems here, your suggested solution:

_____

_____

_____

b. I feel I am becoming all God meant for me to be.

1	2	3	4	5	6	7	8	9	10
Rarely				Some of the time					Always

Please explain: _____

_____

_____

If there are problems here, your suggested solution:

_____

_____

_____

c. I feel secure, protected, and provided for.

1	2	3	4	5	6	7	8	9	10
Rarely				Some of the time					Always

Please explain: _____

_____

_____

there are problems here, your suggested solution:

_____

_____

_____

Interact As a Couple—45 Minutes

1. Begin by reading Ephesians 4:29–32 together.

2. WIVES: Share your completed project with your husband in a way that makes no demands but which promotes positive communication about your three areas of need.

3. Decide together which of these three areas needs the most immediate attention. Then decide on one practical step that you as a husband can take *now* to better meet this need.

_____

_____

_____

Please be sure you agree on this action step and how it will be implemented.

4. Close your time in prayer, committing this action step to the Lord.

Remember to bring your calendar for **MAKE A DATE** to the next session.

Men are, by creation, different from women. These differences generate special needs. . . needs which a wife is uniquely called upon to fulfill.

1. Husbands, from your time on **HomeBuilders Project #2**, share one specific way you've chosen to love your wife differently than before.

_____

_____

_____

2. What is the most significant insight you have gained so far concerning men, women, their differences, and marriage?

_____

_____

_____

What Is It That Men Need Most?

In Session Two the wives were given the opportunity to discuss their needs as women. Now it's the husband's turn. HUSBANDS: What do you think are your special needs as a man? Record helpful comments below, then see if some general agreement can be found by the men as to your three greatest needs. WIVES: Listen carefully. EVERYONE: Take notes.

_____

_____

_____

Your Top Three Choices Are:

_____

_____

_____

II. What the Bible Has to Say

A. The Major Needs of Men and Women

The Scripture reveals that what a man needs most from a woman in marriage is strikingly different from what a woman needs most from a man. In the last session, Paul's letter to the Ephesians helped us see what a wife needs from her husband. It can be summed up in one word:

_____ (Ephesians 5:25)

In this same chapter, another single word sums up what a husband consistently needs from his wife. Read Ephesians 5:33 and record this key word which Paul selects:

_____

B. The Importance of Respect to a Man

Many men are not aware of how important respect is to them. Some women may not be aware of it either. Before going further, let's brainstorm over what this word respect actually means. What other words come to mind when you think of this word "respect"? A dictionary definition might be a helpful place to begin.

_____   _____

_____   _____

_____   _____

Now put some additional "color" into this word by thinking of it in terms of a wife's responsiveness to her husband. What would respect look like to you in the everyday of a marriage relationship?

_____   _____

_____   _____

_____   _____

However a man may appear, his nature is basically insecure. Often a man's masculinity is more fragile than a woman's femininity . . . his self-esteem is more easily threatened. Men, more than women, have a need to "prove" themselves, for doubts are always lingering. The view a man has of himself (whether good or bad) is usually a reflection fro:

two sources: his work and his woman. If either of these become shaky, so do his feelings and perceptions about his manhood. Depression and anger often fill such times. A wife's ongoing responsiveness to her husband should be a well from which a husband can draw respect for himself. His self-respect is, in many ways, her respect reborn in him.

II. Three Valuable Ways a Wife Can "Respect" Her Husband

A. By Honoring and Esteeming Him

How does Proverbs 12:4 picture the impact a wife can have on her husband?

_____

_____

What does a crown signify? How would wearing a crown suddenly change the perception others had of you? How would it raise your own self-perception?

_____

_____

Paul uses this same figure in expressing his feelings about the believers in Thessalonica. They were his "crown." What words did Paul use in 1 Thessalonians 2:19–20 to describe the impact these believers had on his life?

_____

_____

These same words would apply when a wife is the "crown" of her husband.

4. HUSBANDS: List one or two occasions in which your wife has been like a crown to you. Describe your feelings on such occasions.

_____

_____

5. Look back at Proverbs 12:4. Although this verse says a wife can be like a crown to her husband, it also indicates that a wife also possesses the power to "shame" her husband. The phrase "shames him" speaks o. disrespect or public embarrassment. It has overtones of making one either feel or become worthless.[1] What are some ways women can undercut their husbands, making them feel worthless or embarrassed? Publicly? Privately?

HUSBANDS: You will need to take the lead in helping to answer this question.

_____

_____

6. WIVES: What gracious "words of praise" would your husband love to hear from you that would honor him and give him a greater sense of his value as a man? (see Proverbs 16:24). List some below.

_____   _____

_____   _____

_____   _____

1. _Nelson's Expository Dictionary of the Old Testament_ (Nashville: Thomas Nelson Publishers, 1980), p. 371.

B. By Supporting (and Not Competing with) Him

. Notice the support the "excellent wife" of Proverbs 31:10–12 gives o her husband. What specific insights about her are revealed in hese verses?

_____

_____

. What does Proverbs 21:9, 19 say about a wife who competes with er husband?

_____

_____

. HUSBANDS: Share one area of your life where your wife's support irectly contributed to your success. Be sure to include how and why did so.

_____

_____

WIVES: In what specific area could your husbands use more support om you? How could your active support (rather than passivity, "iticism, inflexibility, resistance, etc.) make a difference?

_____

_____

C. By Physically Responding to Him

w areas affirm a man as a man as does his wife's sexual sponsiveness to him. Spontaneous hugs and kisses or other emonstrations of affection, as well as lovemaking, all do more than st give pleasure. These things reassure a man . . . they confirm m in his masculinity.

1. Notice as an example the responsiveness of the Shulamite bride to Solomon (Song of Solomon 7:10–12). HUSBANDS: How would you feel at such words? How does this communicate respect?

_____

_____

2. HUSBANDS: How has your wife's physical responsiveness positively affected your view of yourself? Explain.

_____

_____

_____

> **HomeBuilders Principle #4: Other than a man's relationship with the Lord, few things tell a man more about himself than does the respect of his wife.**

IV. Summary

A respectful wife is life-giving to a man. He draws from her a strong and affirmative sense of who he is. Clearly a wife can brighten her husband's life by her admiration and esteem. She can stabilize his life by her supportiveness. She can also energize his life by her physical responsiveness. In short, she is called to fulfill many of his deepest needs through the simple admonition: **"See to it that you respect your husband"** (Ephesians 5:33).

(to be completed as a couple)

There has been much research in the area of adult male development. It has been documented that all men have a common pattern underlying their lives.[2] Each man's adult life consists of stages, each lasting roughly 20-25 years. These stages overlap at points called "transitions," meaning that as one stage is ending, a new one is getting underway.

1. Separately look over the **Adult Male Life Cycle** charted on the pages that follow.

2. Focus *on that stage* which is relevant to you as a man (and to you as a couple).

3. In the space provided on the right side of the chart, list practical ways a wife's respect (as defined in this session) would cause her husband to succeed in that particular stage of his life with its unique pressures and stresses.

4. Share your feelings and conclusions with one another after you have recorded your thoughts.

5. If you find you need more interaction time, then begin the **HomeBuilders Project** by finishing up any incomplete discussion.

Material adapted here is based on the extensive research done by Daniel Levinson and published in his book, *Seasons of a Man's Life* (New York: Ballantine Books), 1978.

ADULT MALE LIFE CYCLE

Early Adulthood—	Early to Middle Adult Transition	—Middle Adulthood—	Middle to Late Adult Transition	—Late Adulthood

| Age 20 | 40 | 45 | 60 | 65 | + + |

CHARACTERISTICS OF STAGES AND TRANSITIONS

Stage	Characteristics	How a Woman's Respect Helps . . .
Early Adulthood (20–40)	Struggle to establish self in society . . . *Starting* is the key word (job, marriage, family, home, etc.). A time for men to dream. A time of stress, doubt, insecurity. Usually a stressful vocational move is made around 30 as a man seeks to position himself for the future.	
Early to Middle Adult Transition (40–45)	Major turning point as life shifts from youth to middle age. Temptation to reclaim neglected parts of youth stage which now seek expression (sometimes urgently). A pivotal period of inner evaluation, psychologically stressful . . . appraising self in relation to job, marriage, meaning, etc. Must come to terms with questions such as "What have I done?"; "Where am I now?"; "Of what value is my life . . . to others, to society, to me?" This period can produce extreme crisis and even panic behavior . . . the infamous midlife crisis.	

52

CHARACTERISTICS OF STAGES AND TRANSITIONS (Continued)

Stage	Characteristics	How a Woman's Respect Helps . . .
Middle Adulthood (45–60)	Based upon the previous transition, a sense of a new beginning or a growing sense of regression, stagnation, or even failure. Distinct sense of bodily decline and the passing away of youth. Ever-growing sense of mortality. The quality and character of the rest of a man's life is usually determined here.	
Middle to Late Adulthood Transition (60–65)	Decreasing vigor and capacity; coming to terms with what this now means. Moving off center stage can be traumatic to some—less recognition, authority, and power. "Who am I now?"—deep struggle of reappraisal.	
Late Adulthood (65+)	Retirement . . . a time of satisfaction and serenity or bitterness, disappointment, resentment, and fear. A time closely connected to the decisions and events of middle adulthood. "What can I do now?"	

Make a date with your mate to meet in the next
few days to complete **HomeBuilders Project #3.**

_____	_____	_____
Date	Time	Location

■

(for wives only)

■ **Creative Counterpart**   by Linda Dillow

A creative counterpart is more than just a helper. She is a woman who
having chosen a vocation of wife and mother, decides to learn and
grow in all the areas of this role. Linda Dillow tells how to become such
a person in this unique book that is entertaining, practical, and
biblically based.

■

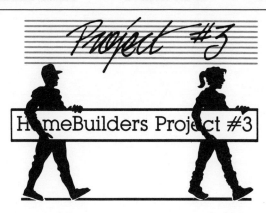

Individually—10–15 Minutes

1. WIFE: Review carefully Session Three.

2. HUSBAND: Complete the following project, circling the numbers that apply and filling in the blanks:

Because of my wife's respect . . .

1. I feel honored and esteemed as a man.

1	2	3	4	5	6	7	8	9	10
Rarely				Some of the time					Always

Please explain: _____

_____

_____

If there are problems here, your suggested solution:

_____

_____

_____

b. I feel supported and encouraged as a man.

1	2	3	4	5	6	7	8	9	10
Rarely				Some of the time					Always

Please explain: _____

_____

_____

If there are problems here, your suggested solution:

_____

_____

_____

c. I feel physically affirmed as a man.

1	2	3	4	5	6	7	8	9	10
Rarely				Some of the time					Always

Please explain: _____

_____

_____

If there are problems here, your suggested solution:

_____

_____

_____

Interact As a Couple—25-30 Minutes

1. Begin by reading **again** Ephesians 4:29–32.

2. HUSBANDS: Share your completed project with your wife in a way that makes no demands but which promotes clear communication about your three areas of need.

3. Decide together which of these three areas needs the most immediate attention. WIVES: Discuss with your husband one practical step you can take now to better meet this need.

_____

_____

_____

Please be sure you agree on this action step and how it will be implemented.

4. Close your time in prayer, committing this action to the Lord.

Remember to bring your calendar for **MAKE A DATE** to the next session.

The HomeBuilders

C O U P L E S   S E R I E S

"Unless the Lord builds the house,
they labor in vain who build it."
Psalm 127:1

Focus

*The Bible sets forth specific roles
for men and women in marriage.
Any couple serious about pleasing God
will seek to shape their marriage
around these general role responsibilities.
For the man, the divine challenge
is to be a servant-leader.*

1. Privately, list three leaders whom you have come to admire greatly. In your mind, what made them both great and effective?

_____

_____

2. Share your conclusions with the rest of the group.

3. What are the qualities that made Jesus a great leader? What qualities seem to stand out above the rest? Record your group's insights in the spaces below.

_____

_____

_____

_____

_____

I. An Overall Perspective on Roles

A. There are no role-less marriages. In time, every marriage will settle into some social and organizational arrangement causing both husband and wife to play specific roles which uphold it. What structure a couple ultimately decides upon depends upon which "voices" they consider authoritative. Review the list of voices below that are so powerfully influential in the structuring of a marriage and the roles people play. Rank them 1–6, using #1 to represent the *most* influential authority behind your own marriage and #6 as the *least* influencial one.

__3__ How I saw my parents live out their marriage

__5__ What I have "absorbed" from today's culture

__4__ How my peers have chosen to live out their marriages

__2__ The Bible

__1__ What I have read in books, studied, seen, etc.

____ Other sources: _____

Compare your list with your spouse's list.

Share with the group which "voice" has influenced your marriage the most. The least? Explain.

_____

_____

3. What warning does Psalm 127:1 give to any couple regarding the structure of their marriage?

_____

_____

B. A Very Important Announcement

There is *great* misunderstanding concerning the roles of men and women today. Therefore, it is extremely important that you not jump to conclusions about what a session will teach beforehand. The titles selected for a husband's role and a wife's role in the next session should be considered as "core" roles and not "comprehensive" lifestyles. In other words, these roles for husbands and wives, though essential to a marriage, are not all one does in the marriage. It would be a great mistake, for instance, to conclude that the role

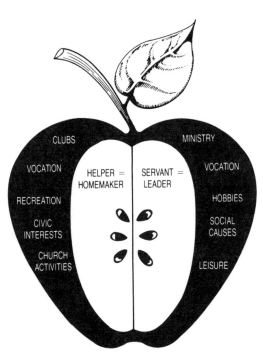

abel "helper-homemaker" in Session Five is meant to imply that all a woman does is "stay at home and submit to her husband." This is an understandable reaction in light of our culture, but unfair and inaccurate to the truth soon to be addressed in these sessions. There is great latitude, creativity, and flexibility around one's core role. There is also great danger in ignoring these core roles, altering them, or violating them. Throughout the next two sessions, you will do well to remember this word *core* as opposed to *comprehensive*. We are addressing the core structure of your marriage, not the entire lifestyle of a man or a woman.

II. God's Core Role for Husbands

For the husband is the head of the wife, as Christ also is the head of the church, He Himself being the Savior of the body (Ephesians 5:23).

A. Misunderstandings of Headship

What is your present understanding of Paul's statement, "the husband is the head of the wife"?[1] Does the thought of "privilege" or "responsibility" first come to mind? What feelings surface with this statement?

_____

_____

Historically, it should be noted that Paul's statement in Ephesians 5:23 not drawn from a culture where men reigned unchallenged as heads their women. In fact, a serious breakdown of marriage and family was occurring throughout the Roman Empire at this time. Both men and women were resisting the idea that a man was the head of his wife,

---

The word for "head" is to be understood in a figurative sense denoting "leadership of" "having authority over." For a deeper study of the word *head* see the fine discussion of in James B. Hurley's book, *Man and Woman in Biblical Perspective* (Grand Rapids: Zondervan Publishing House, 1981), pp. 144–145, 163–168.

63

Complete sect. 2

but for different reasons. Men really did not want the responsibility; women were increasingly reluctant to give up their "rights." Therefore, Paul's call for a man to be the head of his wife sounded as radical to many then as it does to many now. See 1 Corinthians 11:2, 3. Notice that the Corinthians held "firmly" to all Paul's teaching (v. 2) but obviously struggled over the understanding of headship (v. 3).

3. What dangers or misunderstandings are inherent in the concept of male headship?

_____

_____

_____

> **HomeBuilders Principle #5:** It is crucial that a husband's leadership role be accurately defined before it can be accurately fulfilled.

B. Clarifying the Husband's Leadership Role

1. Notice again Ephesians 5:23. With whom is the husband's leadership style to be compared?

_____

_____

2. Contrasting Leadership Styles

a. How did Jesus express His leadership style in Luke 22:25–27 and Matthew 20:25–28?

And He said to them, "The kings of the Gentiles lord it over them; and those who have authority over them are called 'Benefactors.' But not so with you, but let him who is the greatest among you become as the youngest, and the leader as the servant. For who is greater, the one who reclines at the table, or the one who serves? Is it not the one who reclines at the table? But I am among you as the one who serves" (Luke 22:25-27).

But Jesus called them to Himself, and said, "You know that the rulers of the Gentiles lord it over them, and their great men exercise authority over them. It is not so among you, but whoever wishes to become great among you shall be your servant, and whoever wishes to be first among you shall be your slave; just as the Son of Man did not come to be served, but to serve, and to give His life a ransom for many" (Matthew 20:25-28).

. Describe the "Gentile" leadership style represented in these passages. What key words found in these verses give this kind of leadership its "flavor"?

. Against which of these two leadership styles are women most reacting today?

Using the chart on the following page, contrast the way a "serving leader" and a "lording leader" would handle everyday situations with his wife. Be specific.

The Lording Leader	Situation	The Serving Leader
Example: Buys what pleases ◀ him. Is impulsive. Does not ask for or take into consideration his wife's insight on such a purchase. Overlooks her needs and the needs of his family.	Making a major purchase	*Example:* ▶Deliberates with his wife before making such a decision. Is considerate of her feelings. Exalts the needs of his wife and family above his own.
◀	Responsibilities around the home	▶
◀	Disciplining the children	▶
◀	Arriving at a difficult decision	▶
◀	Listening to his wife's suggestions	▶
◀	Handling finances	▶
◀	Spiritual initiatives: prayer, church, Bible study, etc.	▶
◀	Scheduling	▶

III. Three Leadership Responsibilities for Servant-Leaders

Complete the following statements in your own words by reading the passages of Scripture associated with them. Discuss what each of these statements would look like in the everyday of a marriage. Then list practical suggestions a man could take to enhance his leadership performance in each area:

66

He must be one who manages his own household well, keeping his children under control with all dignity (1 Timothy 3:4).

A. A servant-leader will _____ his household well.

Practical ideas: _____

_____

_____

And, fathers, do not provoke your children to anger; but bring them up in the discipline and instruction of the Lord (Ephesians 6:4; see also Deuteronomy 6:6–7).

B. A servant-leader will _____ his children.

Practical ideas: _____

_____

_____

Do not merely look out for your own personal interests, but also for the interests of others. Have this attitude in yourselves which was also in Christ Jesus (Philippians 2:4, 5).

C. A servant-leader will _____ his wife.

Practical ideas: _____

_____

_____

IV. Perspectives for Wives

A. The Wife Is Subject to Her Husband

1. This session has focused on the role of a husband as a leader. But what implications are there for the wife in this regard? Read again Ephesians 5:22–24, this time spotlighting the two verses that come before and after verse 23. What do these verses say about a wife's responsiveness?

_____

_____

2. WIVES: How does clarifying and defining the man's core role make the thought of submission easier and more reasonable?

_____

_____

3. HUSBANDS: Does your leadership make your wife's submission a pleasure or a problem?

_____

_____

> **HomeBuilders Principle #6:** Submission is a woman's spiritual *response* that encourages her husband to fulfill his spiritual role. Submission is essential to the man's success as a servant-leader.

B. Stumbling Blocks to Submission

Notice in Ephesians 5:22 (and elsewhere) that husbands are never told to **make** their wives submit. The appeal to submit in verse 22 is ultimately an issue between a woman and her Lord. Nevertheless, i

s an issue with numerous stumbling blocks and tough questions! For
nstance:

. "What if my husband is not a Christian?" How does 1 Peter 3:1, 2
encourage a wife in this situation?

_____

_____

. "How do I respond to my husband's inconsistencies and failures as a
ervant-leader?" (Colossians 3:12, 13 and Galatians 6:1 would be
.elpful starting places in answering such a question.)

_____

_____

. "What if my husband wants me to do something wrong or illegal?"
[ow does the clarifying phrase attached to the command "be subject
o your husbands" in Colossians 3:18 help in answering this? (See also
le following **Word of Caution #1**.)

_____

_____

"What if I am at times mistreated?" What advice does 1 Peter 3:9–12
ffer?

_____

_____

NOTE: In any extreme case of mistreatment (i.e., physical abuse,
estructive addictions, ongoing adultery, etc.), help should be sought
nmediately. James Dobson's book *Love Must Be Tough*[2] offers helpful
sight for women in such situations.

(Waco, TX: Word Books, 1983).

5. "Isn't submission demeaning to women?" Is it demeaning in
1 Corinthians 11:3 and Ephesians 5:21? (See **Word of Caution #2**.)

WORD OF CAUTION #1: The principle of submission never includes
being asked to disobey other scriptural principles. A man's leadership
over his wife is meant to fulfill the Scripture in their marriage, not
violate it (John 14:15).

WORD OF CAUTION #2: In the name of equality, some women have
sought to challenge or share the leadership role given to their
husbands. A man who properly understands his role biblically will
struggle enough with what that role requires of him. If challenged o
competed with, many men quickly give up and excuse themselves
from their responsibilities. In homes where women seek to lead, men
leave . . . most often they withdraw in psychological, emotional, ar
spiritual ways.

V. Summary

This session has sought to define accurately the role conferred upon
man by God in marriage. It is a position of leadership unique by ar
human standard, primarily because it is so lacking in the "me first"
mentality! Husbands who serve their wife and children, who seek
their family's best interest, who give direction along biblical
lines—these men are the servant-leaders who lead as they were
intended to. They will rarely lack followers.

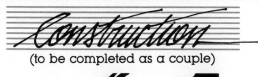

(to be completed as a couple)

1. Wives, write down one illustration from your marriage where your husband has exemplified the servant-leader role as discussed in this session.

_____

_____

2. Husbands, write down how you feel about the role responsibilities set forth in this session. What one adjustment could you make right now that would help in fulfilling the leadership call God has on your life?

_____

_____

3. Share your conclusions with one another.

Make a date with your mate to meet in the next few days to complete **HomeBuilders Project #4**.

Date	Time	Location

■

(for husbands only)

■ **Improving Your Serve**   by Charles Swindol

This book offers accurate, clear, and practical help from the Scriptures on how to develop a servant's heart. The key is a willing heart.

■ **Straight Talk To Men and Their Wives**   by Dr. James Dobso

This book is for every husband who wants to know what it means to be a man: how he should relate to his wife, his children, his work, and his God.

■

Individually—10–15 Minutes

1. Review this session in its entirety.

2. Concentrate specifically on the three leadership responsibilities for servant-leaders (Section III), reviewing and recalling the comments made by the group.

Interact As a Couple—30–40 Minutes

1. Discuss together these three areas of responsibility, then agree upon one that, at present, you both feel needs attention and further refinement.

2. Answer specifically the following questions:

1. HUSBAND: What practical steps can you now take as a result of this discussion with your wife which would demonstrate to her the role of a servant-leader?

_____

_____

b. WIFE: What helpful expression of submissiveness could you offer to your husband's effort that would both affirm and encourage him in his leadership role?

_____

_____

3. Commit to a plan of action.

4. Conclude with a time of prayer together. You might specifically . . .

a. Thank God for outlining in His Word how a marriage is to work (Proverbs 16:20).

b. Confess your failures in your marriage, knowing that He is always ready to forgive (1 John 1:9).

c. Ask His help so that you might succeed in the plan of action just determined (Proverbs 16:3, 9).

d. Praise Him that He will never leave you nor forsake you (Hebrews 13:5).

Remember to bring your calendar for **MAKE A DATE** to the next session.

A woman's role in marriage, though
different from a man's, is equally
important. For her, the divine
challenge is that of being a
helper-homemaker.

1. There is much controversy today concerning a woman's role. If you could see the contemporary family acted out on a stage, would the woman's role be that of:

_____ The Heroine   _____ The Martyr

_____ The Victim   _____ The Extra

_____ The Villain   _____ _____

2. Check one and tell why.

_____

_____

_____

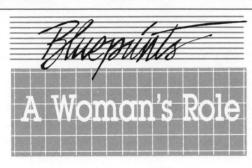

I. God's Core Role for Wives

A. Define a core role. _____

_____

_____

B. What distinctions were made between "core roles" and "comprehensive lifestyles" in Session Four?

_____

_____

_____

_____

HomeBuilders Principle #7: It is crucial that a wife's role as helper and homemaker be accurately defined before it can be accurately fulfilled.

II. Defining the Role of Helper-Homemaker

A. The Wife As "Helper"

Then the Lord God said, "It is not good for the man to be alone; I will make him a helper suitable for him" (Genesis 2:18).

1. Helper: Negatives and Positives

a. What words immediately come to mind when you think of a woman as a man's "helper"?

_____

_____

b. Do these words have a positive or negative connotation in your mind?

_____

_____

2. Helper: A Title for God

a. The title of "helper" given to a woman in Genesis 2 is also a title given to God. For example, God is our "Helper" in Psalm 10:14 and in Isaiah 41:10, 13, 14. What new perspective does this fact give in understanding a wife's helper role?

_____

_____

. What new dignity does it give?

_____

_____

. The Godly Wife

1. Review again how the husband of Proverbs 31 is helped by his wife
(according to vv. 10–12). How would verse 12 be demonstrated in
practical, everyday ways today?

_____

_____

. What impact did this woman's assistance have on her husband's
public life, according to Proverbs 31:23? In your opinion, how is this
success the result of her help? Explain.

_____

_____

HUSBANDS: In what ways has your wife been a valued source of
help to you? Has it been her trusted counsel? Insight? Work? What? How
has she filled up the "gaps" in your life?

_____

_____

WIVES: In what areas do you see yourself as especially "suited" to be
your husband's helper?

_____

_____

5. As far as the godly wife is concerned, how is the title "competitor" the opposite of "helper?"

_____

_____

6. Secrets of Success

a. Some wives are better at helping their husbands than other wives. What is their "secret of success" according to Proverbs 31:30?

_____

_____

b. What is the "secret of success" found in Proverbs 19:14?[1]

_____

_____

_____

B. The Wife As "Homemaker"

1. Titus 2:4–5 puts forth a practical list of core role activities for a wife part of which addresses her involvement at home. What are they?

_____

_____

2. Why would the older wives be best suited to "encourage" the younger wives in this direction?

_____

_____

1. "Prudent" in this passage means using good judgment, intelligence, and common sense in practical matters.

3. Using the historical footnote on this page, tell why the word *encourage* in Titus 2:4 is so appropriate for this time?[2] What does all this tell you about women, their pursuits, and their interests in the first century?

_____

_____

4. Encouragement for the Homemaker

A. WIVES: Are you being encouraged to give time and attention to your home and family?

_____

_____

B. Who or what are the sources of your encouragement?

_____

_____

The following historical snapshots are enlightening in regard to the women of the first century:

"Emancipation (for women) was as complete then as now. . . . Women worked in shops, or factories, especially in the textile trades; some became lawyers and doctors; some became politically powerful. . . . the decay of the ancient faith among the upper classes had washed away the supernatural supports of marriage, fidelity, and parentage; the passage from farm to city had made children less of an asset, more of a liability, and a toy; women wished to be sexually beautiful rather than maternally beautiful." Will Durant, *The Story of Civilization: Caesar and Christ, Vol. III* (New York: Simon & Schuster, 1944), p. 222, 370.

Before the New Testament age, in the old Roman Republic, "a woman took pride in her fertility." Now, in the time of Jesus and Paul, "she fears it." Women at this time "were not content to live their lives by their husbands' sides." Jerome Carcopino, *Daily Life In Ancient Rome* (New Haven: Yale University Press, 1966), p. 93.

c. Who or what are the sources of your discouragement?

_____

_____

5. The Homemaker's Relevance

a. ". . . that the word of God may not be dishonored" (Titus 2:5). How does this phrase indicate that Paul's emphasis on being at home and with family is more than a mere cultural one, relevant only to the women of the first century?

_____

_____

b. How does Isaiah 40:8 further support Paul's statement?

_____

_____

6. The Godly Wife

a. Let's go back to the "exalted wife" of Proverbs 31. What statement is given about her regarding her home in v. 27?

_____

_____

b. Notice the phrase "looks well." It implies attention, creativity, and care. WIVES: How much time does it take for you to look after your home and children in an attractive, creative, and careful way?

_____

_____

USBANDS: How much time do you think it takes?

_____

_____

What kind of response does this quality homemaker draw out of oth her husband and children according to Proverbs 31:28–29?

_____

_____

II. Perspectives for Husbands

iis session has focused on the role of a woman as a helper-omemaker. But what are the implications associated with this role r the husband? What response is required of him as she seeks to lfill the charge God has given to her?

A. Circle the key words in the verses printed below which escribe the kind of response a wife needs from her husband.

Render to all what is due them . . . honor to whom honor (is due) (Romans 13:7).

Her husband . . . praises her, saying: "many daughters have done nobly, but you excel them all!" (Proverbs 31:28).

". . . and grant her honor as a fellow heir of the grace of life" (1 Peter 3:7).

B. HUSBANDS: How are such responses crucial to your wife's success in pursuing her biblical role? Why are they especially important in today's world?

_____

_____

C. WIVES: Share with the men some practical ways they could meaningfully encourage you in your role. Tell them why you need this, how often, and how valuable it is to your daily perspective. HUSBANDS: Take notes!

_____

_____

_____

> **HomeBuilders Principle #8: Honor and praise are the masculine counterparts to submission. They are essential to the wife's success as a helper-homemaker.**

IV. Summary

How a woman views her husband and her home is not only a statement of her values but also the source of her values. It is clear from Scripture that a wife plays a unique role in her husband's success as a man. He needs a "helper," and without his wife's special attention, he is prone to imbalances and blind spots. It is equally clear that God intended for the home and those within it to be a woman's core concern. Though a husband is called to provide for and manage a home, it is the wife's special calling to _make_ it a home. These divine challenges are at the heart of her calling as a wife.

(to be completed as a couple)

This **CONSTRUCTION** time offers you a choice of *two* alternatives. The first project is more general in nature, overviewing this session as a whole. The second project is much more specific. It focuses on the struggle some wives who work outside the home have in balancing their career with their core calling. As a couple, choose the project that best applies to your situation. If you need more time than the construction sequence allows, start off your **HomeBuilders Project** by finishing up any incomplete discussion.

Project Alternative One

1.   HUSBANDS: Write down one illustration from your marriage where your wife has exemplified the helper-homemaker role discussed in this session.

_____

_____

. what specific area are you presently in need of her help?

_____

_____

2. WIVES: Write down how you feel about the core role responsibilities set forth in this session. What one adjustment could you make right now that would help in fulfilling this domestic call God has on your life?

_____ _____

_____

_____

3. Share your conclusions with one another.

Project Alternative Two

1. As already stated, this project addresses women who work outside the home. The Scriptures, of course, do not expressly prohibit a woman from having a career. In fact, very little is said on this issue. Instead, the Scriptures focus on the priorities, values, and roles that insure success for one's marriage and family. For a wife, the emphasis is on the support of her husband, the priority of her children, and the management of the home. Therefore, these should become the fundamental considerations when addressing work outside the home. They will, as any woman knows, raise serious questions about work that must be squarely faced. WIVES: With the help and interaction of your husbands, answer the following questions.

a. Am I attempting to meet my needs and fulfill my life primarily through a career rather than through my relationship with God, His Word, and the dynamics of my family?

b. Will my husband and children (if any) receive the love and attention they need to succeed?

c. Is there a real need for me to work or is the motivation one of material or personal "wants"?

d. Does my work away from home hinder my ability in fulfilling my core role?

e. Does my husband agree with my desire for a career outside of the home? (A lack of oneness here can be critical.)

f. If applicable, would he be supportive of my desire to return home on a full-time basis?

2. Titus 2:5 exhorts a wife to be "sensible" regarding her life. Clearly, there are "seasons" in a marriage when a vocation outside the home for a woman is more appropriate and sensible than at other times. Consider the following illustration.

A Marriage Life Cycle for Couples with Children

SEASON 1: Married but Without Children	SEASON 2: Pre-Schoolers	SEASON 3: Grade Schoolers thru High School	SEASON 4: College Age: Some Children Still at Home	SEASON 5: The Empty Nest

a. As a couple, evaluate in which seasons work outside the home would best complement God's role call on a wife. In which seasons would outside work tend to conflict most with God's call? How do these observations apply to your present situation?

_____

_____

b. What reminder does Proverbs 14:1 give as a woman addresses these questions and considerations of work and family?

_____

_____

c. What, if any, action steps do you need to take as a result of this discussion?

_____

_____

87

Make a date with your mate to meet in the next few days to complete **HomeBuilders Project #5**.

Date	Time	Location

■

(for wives only)

■ **What Is a Family?**   by Edith Schaeffe

In an age when the survival of the family as a living, loving unit is being threatened as never before, Edith Schaeffer presents a heartening view of family life. Written with rare insight and empathy, **What Is a Family?** explores the problems and challenges facing all Christians today, offering hope and encouragement to those who treasure the values of family life.

■ **A Mother's Heart**   by Jean Flemin

This book tells how you can take a spiritual inventory of your child, how to thoughtfully pray for him, creatively love him, and teach him about who God is and what He teaches about life.

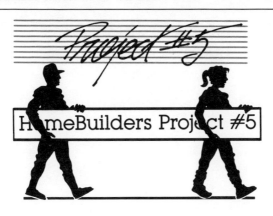

Individually—10–15 Minutes

1. Review this session in its entirety. Concentrate specifically on the helper and homemaker aspects of the wife's role.

2. HUSBANDS: How often do you praise your wife for the special role she plays in your life and the lives of your children? Record in the space below how and how often you have honored her for specifically being a helper, mother, and homemaker.

_____

_____

_____

_____

WIVES: Try to remember times when your husband has so honored you.

_____

_____

_____

Interact As a Couple—30–40 Minutes

1. Which of the two aspects of a wife's role do you both feel at present needs attention and further refinement?

_____

_____

2. Answer the following questions:

a. WIVES: What *practical* steps can you define that would address the area of concern identified in Question 1?

_____

_____

b. HUSBANDS: What word of praise or act of honor could you attach to your wife's effort that would affirm, motivate, and encourage her in her helper-homemaker role?

_____

_____

_____

3. Conclude with a time of prayer together.

Remember to bring your calendar for **MAKE A DATE** to the next session.

Every man and woman has a natural resistance to resolving their gender differences and fulfilling the roles and responsibilities set forth in Scripture for their marriage. Therefore, a supernatural effort is required for God's calling on a marriage to be realized.

1 . Below is a succinct summary of this **HomeBuilders** study so far. As you review it, what specific insights, key scriptures, and principles from the past five sessions does the outline bring to mind? Record these recollections in the space below the chart.

ISSUES	HUSBAND	WIFE
Resolving Gender Differences	Understands the Feminine Viewpoint	Understands the Masculine Viewpoint
Special Needs	Respect	Love
Core-Role Responsibility	Servant-Leader	Helper-Homemaker
Response Needed from Mate That Encourages Role Fulfillment	Submission	Honor and Praise
Results Promised:	**Oneness in Marriage**	**Oneness in Marriage**

_____

_____

_____

_____

2. Share your insights with the group.

3. Conclude your **WARM UP** time by focusing on the items listed under "issues" in the previous diagram. If someone were available to help you significantly improve one of these issues (resolving gender differences, role responsibility, etc.) which one would you choose to improve? Indicate your selection by marking it with an **X**.

I. God **Has** Given Us a Supernatural "Helper" to Help Us Succeed in Marriage

A. In the previous sessions, we have been exploring God's blueprints for marriage. God, however, is not content to just give us these much-needed directions. He also offers His personal assistance in getting the job done.

1. What promise does Jesus make to His followers in John 14:16–18?

_____

_____

2. What is another name for this Helper in verse 17? _____

In verse 26? _____

3. The help Jesus promised that the Spirit would give to the disciples for their lives is the same help the Spirit offers to us for our marriages. What is this very special assistance as stated in v. 26?

_____

_____

3. How could you see this kind of help being manifested and experienced in your marriage? How would it make a difference? Can you give a personal example?

_____

_____

_____

_____

> **HomeBuilders Principle #9: The Holy Spirit will be faithful to remind us of God's Word if we are faithful in learning it.**

II. What Hinders the Helper

A. Within every man and woman there is an evil impulse that rejects God's directions and resists God's help. This streak of independence (Isaiah 53:6) found its way into the heart of humanity when Adam and Eve first disobeyed God (Romans 5:12). It has been passed along to all subsequent generations.

Resistance to God's Plan

1. How does Romans 8:5–8 express this natural resistance?

_____

_____

What label does Paul use here to describe this resistance?

_____

How the Flesh Manifests
Itself in a Marriage

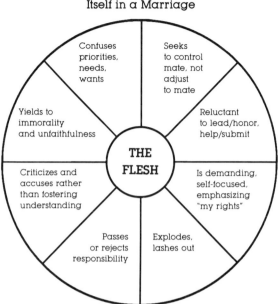

2. How is "the flesh" further described in Galatians 5:19–21?

_____

_____

_____

3. The Power of This Resistance

a. Using Romans 7:18–21 as a reference point, describe how the flesh influences those seeking to construct their marriage according to God's blueprints.

_____

_____

b. In what ways have you experienced the fruit of the flesh limiting the success of your marriage? (Resist pointing fingers . . . personalize.)

_____

_____

_____

> **HomeBuilders Principle #10: The fuel that most often energizes the flesh is our world (1 John 2:15–16/Jude 19).**

3. Overcoming the Flesh

a. God has placed His Holy Spirit within every Christian so that the power of the flesh can be opposed and overcome. Having two opposing forces within us creates an ongoing internal conflict which most of us feel every day. Notice how this conflict is expressed in Galatians 5:16–17.

_____

_____

Therefore, in the heart of every Christian is the same struggle:

97

2. The daily ongoing skirmishes that take place between the flesh and God's Spirit do not in themselves determine the outcome. In other words, who wins in your heart and ultimately in your life is not determined by those forces alone. *Who wins is determined by you . . . by an act of your will!* It is your choice that unleashes either the power of the flesh or the power of the Spirit to influence and rule in that moment of your life . . . and then in the next moment . . . and the next.

a. How does Paul make it clear that our choice is the determining factor . . .

in Romans 6:12, 13?

_____

_____

in Romans 8:12, 13?

_____

_____

b. How does Moses say it in Deuteronomy 30:19?

_____

_____

How the Holy Spirit Manifests
Himself in a Marriage

. If we choose to yield ourselves to the influence of God's Spirit, what
will be the powerful results? See Galatians 5:22, 23.

_____

_____

_____

When we submit to God's Spirit, good things happen!

HomeBuilders Principle #11: The Holy Spirit helps fulfill in us
what God requires of us in marriage.

4. Describe one instance in your marriage where you believe you have yielded to God's Spirit and experienced the fruit and power He promised.

_____

_____

_____

HomeBuilders Principle #12: The fuel that most often energizes the Spirit is God's Word (2 Timothy 3:16–17/Colossians 3:16a).

III. Releasing God's Power in Your Marriage

A. Releasing God's power in your marriage depends on several factors:

1. It depends on whom I believe is right—God's Word or the flesh.

2. It depends on whose voice I listen to—the voice of the Spirit or the voice of my flesh.

3. It depends on whom I love the most—God or the flesh.

4. Finally and most important, it depends in the end on whom I yield and submit to—God's Spirit or the flesh.

B. This form of submission is for every Christian husband and wife! It is a submission that crowns a marriage with God's blessing. When a man and woman submit to the Holy Spirit—who is seeking to apply God's Word to a marriage—then God's power is released.

This submission is not to be thought of as a one-time event, but a moment-by-moment walk with God and struggle against the flesh.

HomeBuilders Principle #13: A husband and wife can resolve gender differences, respond to unique needs, and fulfill respective roles only as they submit by faith to God's Spirit and live under His special influence (Ephesians 5:18).

(to be completed as a couple)

1. What new understanding of your marriage do you now have as a result of this session on the Holy Spirit?

_____

_____

2. What one area in your lives needs the powerful influence of the Holy Spirit right now?

_____

_____

3. In light of the session, how would you expect the Holy Spirit to give you realistic help in this area? How would He make a difference?

_____

_____

_____

4. What could you do to help the Holy Spirit help you?

_____

_____

Make a date with your mate to meet in the next few days to complete **HomeBuilders Project #6**.

_____   _____   _____
Date   Time   Location

■

Recommended Reading

The Holy Spirit   by Dr. Bill Bright

In **The Holy Spirit: The Key to Supernatural Living**, Dr. Bill Bright helps you discover the secret of living beyond normal human limits by tapping into the power of God through the Holy Spirit.

Transferable Concepts Books 1-4   by Dr. Bill Bright

- **How to Be Sure You Are a Christian**
- **How to Experience God's Love and Forgiveness**
- **How to Be Filled with the Spirit**
- **How to Walk in the Spirit**

These booklets explain the "how-to's" of consistent, successful Christian living.

As a Couple—25–30 Minutes

1. REVIEW: Share with each other two or three things that really spoke to you from Session Six.

2. What most hinders your walk with the Holy Spirit and keeps you from yielding to His inward promptings? Check one of the choices below, then discuss together.

☐ Pride

☐ Unbelief (Hebrews 11:6)

☐ Being weak to respond to His promptings

☐ Fear (John 10:10)

☐ Ignorance of the Scripture and apparent inability to recognize the "voice" of the Spirit when He speaks (Hebrews 5:13, 14)

☐ Unrepentant sin/guilt (1 John 1:9)

☐ Being in love with the things in the world

☐ My marriage

☐ Ignorance of the Holy Spirit and His ministry

☐ Peer pressure

☐ Other

Individually—15 Minutes

1. Silently read Galatians 5:25.

2. Ask yourself the following questions:

Am I willing to give the Holy Spirit complete control of my life in all areas?

☐ Yes   ☐ No

Am I willing to address aggressively that area which I just indicated most hinders my walk with the Holy Spirit?

☐ Yes   ☐ No

3. If your answer was yes to the questions above, write below the specific steps you intend to take to address that area and when you intend to take each one.

Step	Date

4. Conclude in prayer by telling God what you want to do. Ask for His help in accomplishing your plan. Tell Him you want to know how to walk daily with the Holy Spirit so that your marriage and all of your life will be enriched. Ask God to make you sensitive to the Holy Spirit's personal leading. Say to Him that you are willing for Him to control your life. Commit to God that you will submit to the Holy Spirit when He does so lead. Thank Him by faith that He will answer your prayers.

As a Couple—5–10 Minutes

1. Come back together and share your commitments with one another.

Remember to bring your calendar for **MAKE A DATE** to the next session.

Focus

Marriage is the mold that shapes our children's most basic understanding of themselves. Role and gender confusion in these formative years often has negative consequences in their self-identities for a lifetime. Therefore, a biblical perspective on what it means to be a ``man'' and what it means to be a ``woman,'' demonstrated through the lives of parents, is critical to our children's success.

1. How has this series affected your marriage? List below one change you believe has the best chance of being *long-lasting* in your marriage. Tell why.

_____

_____

_____

2. List below one "gift" ("gifts" being defined as a particular way of life, habit, value, or perspective) that either your mother or father's life has given *you* which has made your marriage better or your role as a husband or wife easier.

_____

_____

_____

_____

3. What is one "gift" you now wish they would have given you? Why?

_____

_____

I. The Law of Lifestyle

A. Identity and Values

. Before parents can impart to their children a clear sense of identity and direction, they must possess these qualities themselves. This is the law of lifestyle. Research has demonstrated that self-esteem and self-confidence, two essential features in the makeup of a child's personality are directly related to parents possessing and communicating a clear idea of what their values are.[1]

Keeping in mind the statement above, which of the following lifestyles would you think most harmful to a child in terms of developing a strong and well-defined sense of self-identity and role? Check one and tell why:

] Parents who communicate Christian values in their marriage and live them out.

] Parents who communicate secular values in their marriage and live them out.

] Parents who communicate Christian values in their marriage and live out secular values.

W. Peter Blitchington, *Sex Roles and the Christian Family* (Wheaton, IL: Tyndale House Publishers, 1981), p. 107.

109

2. How would you apply the story of Luke 6:46–49 to the kind of home you marked? Be specific.

_____

_____

B. Role and Gender Distinctives

1. Role and gender confusion in the next generation is the result of lifestyle confusion in today's homes. It is recycled misery. For children to first notice, then understand, and finally honor basic male and female differences and role patterns, parents must make the golden connection between lips and living. That's the law of lifestyle.

> **HomeBuilders Principle #14: You will leave in your children what you have lived out in your home.**

2. "Parents mold and shape the child's developing personality and give him most of the advantages (or disadvantages) that he will enjoy in later years."[2]

What "advantages" from your marriage would you want to leave your children in light of this series of sessions?

_____

_____

_____

_____

2. Ibid., p. 18.

II. Three "Gifts" for Your Children's Future

A. **Gift #1:** An insightful understanding of the differences and similarities between men and women.

. According to Psalm 119:97–100, 104–105, where should parents go or such insights? Recall what you learned in Session One.

_____

_____

. According to Proverbs 1:8, 9, both Mom and Dad bear responsibility or teaching these vital truths to their children. Of the two, who usually eems to have the greater difficulty in carrying out this responsibility, n your opinion?

_____

_____

. What insight does Psalm 78:5–8 offer in this regard? Who is the ntended recipient of this command?

_____

_____

Compare Psalm 78 with Luke 1:13–17. What is the key to accepting his teaching responsibility?

_____

_____

How is this first gift being given or prepared for right now in your ome? Please describe.

_____

_____

_____

B. **Gift #2:** Practical how-to's in meeting those special needs men and women have.

1. What special needs of women can you recall from our series? List them in the space below. What Scripture can you list next to each which supports your claim that this is a special feminine need?

Special Feminine Need	Scripture
_____	_____
_____	_____
_____	_____
_____	_____

2. HUSBANDS: How would your present lifestyle demonstrate to your children (current or future) that women do have special needs and that you know how to meet them?

_____

_____

HUSBANDS: Take notes on what the other men share. Learn from each other.

3. What special needs did this series reveal men have? List them below and provide a supporting Scripture if you can.

Special Masculine Need	Scripture
_____	_____
_____	_____
_____	_____
_____	_____

4. WIVES: How would your present lifestyle demonstrate to your children (current or future) that men do have special needs and that you know how to meet them?

_____

_____

_____

WIVES: Take notes on what the other wives share. Learn from each other.

C. **Gift #3:** A strong and accurate desire to fulfill one's biblical role in a marriage.

1. For a son that means a desire to be a _____.

   For a daughter that means a desire to be a _____.

2. How would the present role you fill in your marriage, and the attitude with which you do so, create in your son or daughter (current or future) a positive desire for the role God will want them to fill? Explain.

_____

_____

_____

D. Summary

. When we give these "gifts" to our children, we are launching the homes of the future. They will be homes constructed with sound blueprints, clear job descriptions, practical how-to's, and vast potential. How is such a home described in Proverbs 24:3, 4?

_____

_____

2. Notice how these "gifts" extend to bless even our grandchildren in Proverbs 13:20–22b. What other insights does this passage reveal?

_____

_____

III. Gifts That Return

A. Giving such expensive gifts as the ones we have discussed in this session will not go unrewarded in the kingdom of God. "Give, and it will be given to you," Jesus said (Luke 6:38). Gifts that are given will mean gifts that return.

B. In the following references you will find a sampling of what some of these "return gifts" actually are. Discuss your answers.

1. Proverbs 23:24, 25 . . . How do godly children affect the emotional health of a mom and dad in their later years?

_____

_____

Contrast this experience with the one described in Proverbs 17:25.

_____

_____

2. Proverbs 31:10 . . . How would you like to be known for having raised this daughter in your home?

_____

_____

3. Proverbs 31:27–28a . . . How would you as a mother enjoy this kind of acclaim?

_____

_____

4. 3 John 2–4 . . . What is John's greatest joy?

_____

_____

> **HomeBuilders Principle #15: A wise couple knows what life's most promising investments are.**

IV. Summary

ISSUES	HUSBAND	WIFE
Resolving Gender Differences	Understands the Feminine Viewpoint	Understands the Masculine Viewpoint
Special Needs	Respect	Love
Core-Role Responsibility	Servant-Leader	Helper-Homemaker
Response Needed from Mate That Encourages Role Fulfillment	Submission	Honor and Praise
Help Needed from God	Holy Spirit	Holy Spirit
Results Promised:	**Oneness in Marriage "Gifted" Children**	**Oneness in Marriage "Gifted" Children**

Construction

(to be completed as a couple)

1. Proverbs 22:6 is the Bible's basic principle on parenting. What does it say?

_____

_____

What hope does it give?

_____

_____

The word *train* in this passage can also mean "dedicate." It is used of dedicating a home in Deuteronomy 20:5.[3] As parents train their childre. they are actually dedicating the homes of the next generation.

2. For children to be trained rightly, both mom and dad must assume some specific responsibilities. First, look up in the following Scripture the responsibility which applies to you. Record your findings then discuss the questions which follow.

HUSBANDS: Ephesians 6:4

_____

_____

3. Derick Kidner, *Proverbs* (London: Intervarsity Press, 1973), p. 147.

WIVES: Titus 2:3-5

_____

_____

1. Are you willing to assume this responsibility God is asking of you? Why or why not?

_____

_____

2. What are the major stumbling blocks in your minds to fulfilling these parental responsibilities?

_____

_____

3. What changes would you need to begin making right now in order to fulfill these biblical responsibilities?

_____

_____

Make a date with your mate to complete the las **HomeBuilders Project** this week.

Date	Time	Location

■

■ **Sex Roles and the Christian Family**   by Dr. W. Peter Blitchingtc

This is an extraordinary book on family relationships. Here is sound evidence that the biblical plan for marriage, sex, and family living **i** our only hope for integrity and personal fulfillment.

■

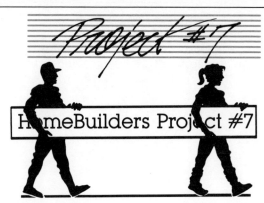

Send a note to your group leader indicating that you have completed the following project.

Individually—10–15 Minutes

Review this last session, summarizing below the major insights that spoke specifically to you and your marriage.

_____

_____

_____

_____

_____

_____

Interact As a Couple—30 Minutes

1. Discuss your summations together. What new insights did you gain?

_____

_____

$2.$ What plan of action can you now commit to as parents (or future parents) as a result of this session? List five specific action steps you plan to take that would "gift" your children in the next generation.

EXAMPLE: Praise my wife regularly in front of my children. Include them in planning special occasions to honor their mother (which hopefully will "gift" sons for honoring their future wives).

Action Step #1: _____

_____

Action Step #2: _____

_____

Action Step #3: _____

_____

Action Step #4: _____

_____

Action Step #5: _____

_____

$3.$ Conclude by reading together Proverbs 16:3. Notice the hope it gives. Use its directions to guide you as you conclude this time in prayer.

Suggested Future Project

We began this session by remembering the "gifts" our parents gave to us that have made our marriages better and easier. Of course they did much more than that . . . much more. Why not take several hours and remember all the good things your parents have done, as well as all the sacrifices they made during your years at home? Write these down. Then organize them into a *written tribute* and present it to one (or both) at a special occasion (their anniversary, Christmas, or a birthday.) Nothing could be more satisfying to a parent than to be remembered and honored in such a way. It will crown the latter part of their life with deep joy. You may find, as many have, that your project is one of your greatest gifts to your parents—one filled with love, healing, and untold blessing.

Honor your Mother and your Father (which is the first commandment with a promise), that it may be well with you, and that you may live long on the earth (Ephesians 6:2, 3).

The HomeBuilders

COUPLES SERIES

"Unless the Lord builds the house,
they labor in vain who build it."
Psalm 127:1

Where do you go from here?

Where Do You Go from Here?

The biblically structured family has probably never been considered "chic." As we learned in this study, it wasn't so in Paul's day, nor is it in ours. Today, a biblically arranged marriage has as many critics as it does skeptics. Even within the Christian community, some have sought to explain it away by using all kinds of fanciful theological arguments. But it will weather these storms just as it has done so generation after generation. God's Word is that clear and certain.

Building your marriage upon these truths may not be popular today, but it will be powerful. Some special glimpses of that power have probably already been felt by you through your investment of study, discussion, and application together. If the truth within this couples study has at times shaken your marriage, it has done so only to strengthen it. Hopefully, a sense of strengthening has been your experience. But let's not stop here!

If this **HomeBuilders Couples Series** study has helped you and your marriage, let's go on. And in going on, why not ask other couples to join you. By personally initiating another **HomeBuilders** study, you will not only add additional mortar to your own marriage, you will also be a part of strengthening other marriages as well. As Christians, we are not just trying to improve ourselves . . . we are trying to reach the world! This is our ultimate objective in **The HomeBuilders Couples Series**. Will you now help us help others?

Will you join us in "Touching Lives . . . Changing Families?"

The following are some practical ways you can make a difference in families today:

1. Gather a group of couples (4–7) and lead them through the seven sessions of the **HomeBuilders** study you just completed.

2. Commit to participate in other **HomeBuilders** studies, such as **Building Your Marriage** or **Strengthening Your Mate's Self-Esteem**.

3. Begin weekly family nights—teaching your children about Christ, the Bible, and the Christian life.

4. Host an Evangelistic Dinner Party—invite your non-Christian friends to your home and as a couple share your faith in Christ and the forgiveness of His Gospel.

5. Share the Good News of Jesus Christ with neighborhood children.

6. If you have attended the Family Life Conference, why not assist your pastor in counseling pre-marrieds using the material you received?

7. Talk with your pastor about renting **The HomeBuilder's Film Series** for your church. This is a six-part series on marriage which is currently available for church showings.

For more information on any of the above ministry opportunities, contact your local church, or write:

Family Ministry
P.O. Box 23840
Little Rock, AR 72221-3840
(501) 223-8663

About the Author:

Robert Lewis has been a teaching pastor at Fellowship Bible Church in Little Rock, Arkansas, since 1980. He is a graduate of the University of Arkansas, Western Conservative Baptist Seminary, and Talbot Theological Seminary. He has spoken nationally and internationally with the Family Ministry of Campus Crusade for Christ for over five years. Robert and his wife, Sherard, have been married for 17 years and have four children: Elizabeth, Rebekah, Garrett, and Mason.

uild Your Marriage by Asking he Right Questions.

The Questions Book by Dennis and Barbara Rainey gives you 31 questions you've never thought to ask your mate. Thirty-one questions that will ignite your curiosity and rekindle your fascination for each other.

A great marriage takes communication and The Questions Book will guide and encourage you and your mate to practice heart-to-heart communication. These questions will spark many memorable hours of sharing, sharpen your understanding of your mate, and stimulate closeness in new areas of your marriage.

The Questions Book…because your marriage is worth it.

uild Your Marriage by uilding Your Mate's elf-Esteem.

nique among human relationships, r marriage has the greatest potential building your mate's self-esteem. It lso the arena in which the greatest ds for self-esteem become evident.

loving to meet this essential need d-on are Dennis and Barbara Rainey, nors of the newly released, Building r Mate's Self-Esteem. In their book, the neys offer you insight into God's self-, self-giving formula for marriage.

s intensely practical book teaches you v to deal with the haunting problems ne past, how to give your mate the dom to fail, how to help your mate iberated from the questions of self-bt and other creative ideas for nediate results.

et your copy today, and learn practical, ven ways to build self-esteem through r marriage.

FAMILY MINISTRY

The HomeBuilders

C O U P L E S   S E R I E S

"Unless the Lord builds the house,
they labor in vain who build it."
Psalm 127:1